The Official Annual

This Peppa Pig book belongs to

....

This book is based on the
TV Series 'Peppa Pig'
'Peppa Pig' is created by
Neville Astley and Mark Baker

Peppa Pig © Astley Baker Davies/
E1 Entertainment 2003

www.peppapig.com

Published by Ladybird Books Ltd 2009
A Penguin Company
Penguin Books Ltd, 80 Strand, London, WC2R 0RL, UK
Penguin Books Australia Ltd, Camberwell, Victoria, Australia
Penguin Books (NZ), 67 Apollo Drive, Rosedale, North Shore
0632, New Zealand (a divison of Pearson New Zealand Ltd)

Contents

Cold Winter Day

It's a chilly day so Peppa and George have wrapped up warm in their hats, scarves and mittens to go and feed the ducks.

"Look, it's a muddy puddle," cries Peppa, who loves jumping in puddles. She runs over to it but as she tries to jump in, she slips! "Oh! It's frozen solid!" she says.

"Hee hee," snorts George.
Peppa says, "It's not funny, George."

She spots Daddy Pig coming towards the puddle. Daddy Pig loves muddy puddles too! Before she can warn him, Daddy Pig has jumped straight onto the frozen puddle.
"Be careful, Daddy!" shout Peppa and George.

"Woah!" says Daddy, wobbling about. "It's lucky I'm so good at balancing."

The little pigs keep walking until they find the duck pond. Peppa and George throw some bread for the ducks, but it just bounces along the surface.

The pond is frozen too and Peppa and George both giggle as the ducks slide around, trying to catch the bread.
"Sorry for laughing, Mrs Duck," says Peppa. "You do look funny!"

"Look! It's snowing," says Daddy Pig. "Some of our friends are tobogganing down the hill. Shall we go and watch?"
"Yes, please!" Peppa and George shout. Daddy picks up George because it's too slippery for him to walk on his own.
"What about me?" says Peppa. "It's a bit slippery for me, too."
"Come on then," says Daddy Pig, scooping up Peppa.

Mummy Pig tells Daddy that he needs to be extra careful not to fall over. "Don't worry, Mummy Pig," he says.
"I'm very good at balancing."
"Hello, Peppa and George," shout Zoe Zebra, Danny Dog and Pedro Pony. "We're going to have a toboggan race!"

"Shall I start you off?" asks Daddy Pig. When the toboggans are all lined up, Daddy Pig shouts, "Ready . . . steady . . . WOAH!" Daddy Pig topples over and starts skidding down the hill! He zooms past Danny, Zoe and Pedro and soon he's in the lead! "Oink, oink!" grunt Peppa and George. They're sitting on Daddy's tummy enjoying the ride.

Peppa and George win the race!
"My daddy makes a great toboggan," Peppa tells everyone. All of the children are laughing about Peppa and George's special toboggan ride.
"It's not funny," says Daddy Pig
"Snort! It is a bit funny," says Mummy Pig.
Erm, I suppose it is a bit funny," Daddy Pig agrees. "Grunt! Grunt! Grunt!"

Snowmen

Peppa and George are building snowmen!
Use your pencils to draw on a face, hat and
scarf to decorate your own snowman.

How many big snowflakes
are in the sky?

10 ....

Slip and Slide

Help Peppa and George ice skate all the way to Mummy and Daddy Pig without crashing!

START

FINISH

11

A Piggy Year

Colour in the tree and find out what Peppa loves most about each of the seasons!

In spring...

the trees are green and flowery.

Put a tick sticker next to things that Peppa can do in spring:

☐ Play in the garden

☐ Open her Christmas presents

☐ Pick flowers

In summer...

the trees are green and shady.

Put a tick sticker next to things that Peppa can do in summer:

☐ Paddle in the sea

☐ Eat an ice lolly

☐ Build a snowman

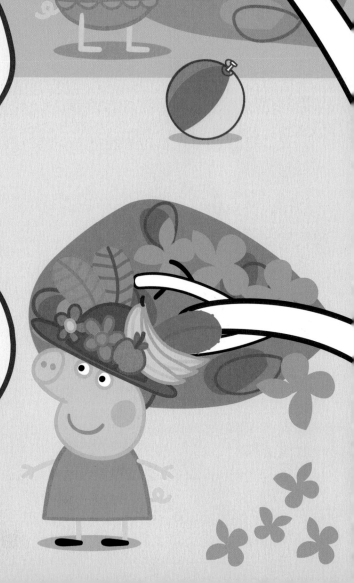

In autumn...

the trees are red and brown.

Put a tick sticker next to things that Peppa can do in autumn:

- ☐ Catch falling leaves
- ☐ Jump in muddy puddles
- ☐ Eat an Easter egg

In winter...

the trees are bare and snowy.

Put a tick sticker next to things that Peppa can do in winter:

- ☐ Play in the paddling pool
- ☐ Go ice skating
- ☐ Wear a hat, scarf and gloves

13

Roaring Drawing

Peppa and George are looking at the dinosaurs in the museum. Draw your own dinosaur, then colour in the picture.

14

Zoom to the Moon

Search this picture of George's space adventure for hidden objects!

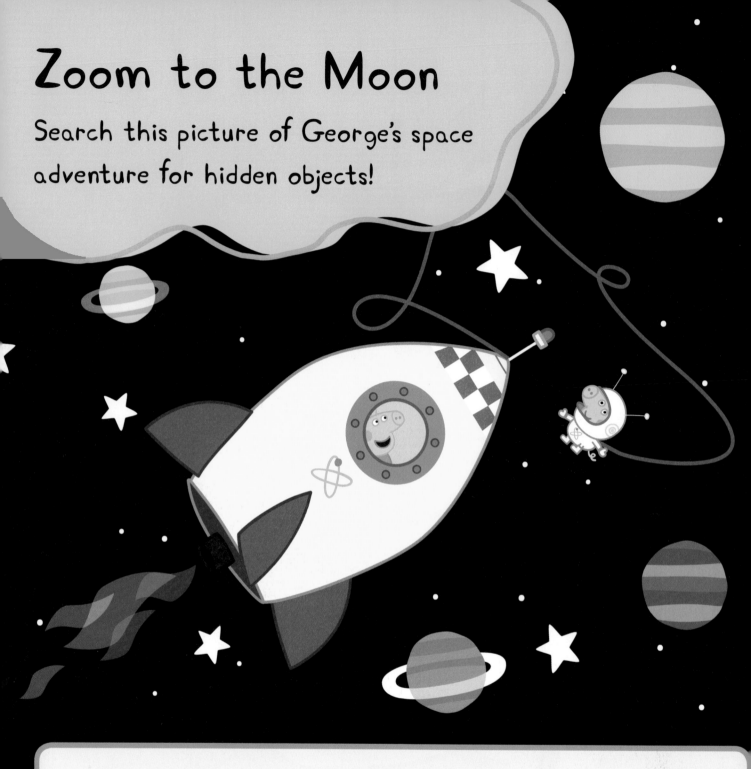

Tick the stars when you find these things in the big picture

 ☆ ☆  ☆  ☆

How many planets can you see? ☐

Piggy Puzzle

Cut along the dotted lines, muddle up the pieces and put them back together. Then turn the pieces over to make a whole new picture!

17

Piggy Puzzle

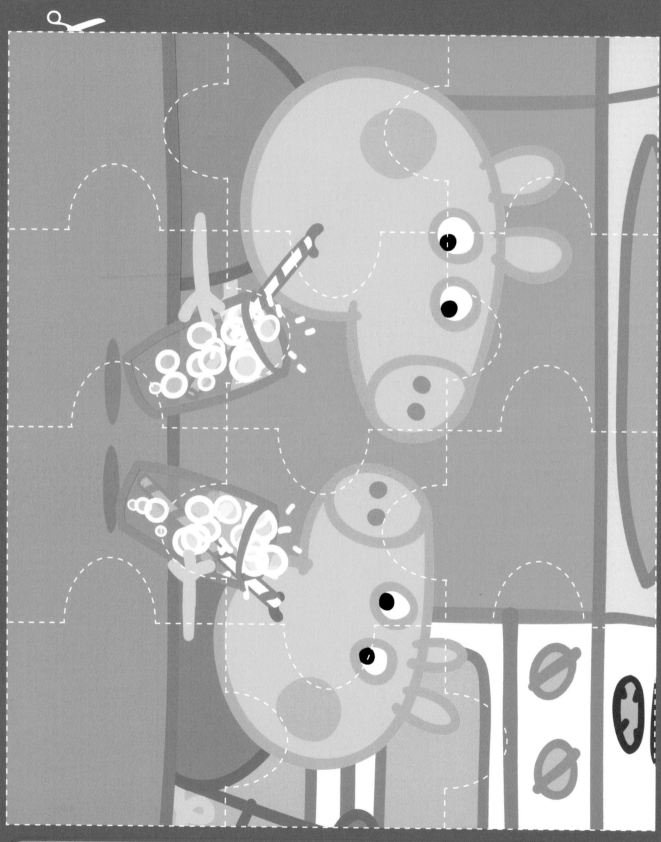

Mr Zebra has found the instructions in his van.
"I'll build it for you," says Mr Zebra.
He quickly puts the toy cupboard together and places the toys inside,
but there's no room for the last two.
"Poor Teddy and Mr Dinosaur, where are they going to live?" cries Peppa.

"I have an idea," begins Mummy Pig. "Teddy and Mr Dinosaur
can live on your beds."
"But that's where they were before," says Peppa.
"I know," smiles Mummy Pig. "That's why it's such a good idea!"

Noisy Toys

Peppa and George make lots of nois[e] when they play! Put the right soun[d] sticker next to each toy.

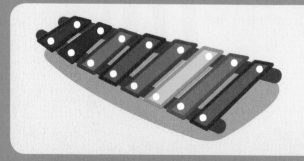

Answers: The monkey goes Oooh! Oooh! the car goes Vroom; the ball goes Bounce Bounce Bounce; the dinosaur goes ROOAAARRR! and the glockenspiel goes Tinkle Tinkle Tinkle.

Brilliant Bookplate

Peppa and George love having stories read to them. Choose which side of this bookplate you like and fill in your name along the dotted lines. Then, cut it out and stick it inside your favourite book!

This brilliant book belongs to

....

This brilliant book belongs to

....

Dotty Dino

Join the dots to finish this big picture of George's favourite toy.

Pop-up Card!

Follow the simple instructions to make this cute Peppa pop-up card and give it to a friend!

You will need:

Safe scissors

Glue

Thin card

What to do:

1. When you've finished reading this book, pull out the page opposite and stick it onto thin card.
2. Cut out the car, background and tab along the dotted lines and fold along the straight lines.
3. Glue tab 'a' to box 'a' on the background, then attach the car, by glueing 'b' to 'b'.
4. Finally, glue tab 'c' to the back of the car and your card is finished!

Now, give your card to someone very special!

Oooh! Oooh! Oooh!

Tinkle Tinkle Tinkle

Bounce Bounce Bounce

Vrrooom Vrrooom

P

A B

Oink!

Pages 12-13

To:

a

b

From:

a

c

b

To

Peppa's Birthday Wish

Peppa is blowing out the candles on her birthday cake. What do you think she is wishing for? Draw Peppa's birthday wish inside the thought bubble below.

Pretend Friend

Suzy Sheep has come to Peppa Pig's house to play. Suzy has brought her new friend, Leo Lion. But Peppa can't see Leo anywhere! She asks Suzy if Leo would like to be her friend too. "Roar!" says Suzy. "That means, yes!"

Mummy Pig has cut two slices of fruit cake for Peppa and Suzy. "Don't forget about Leo," says Suzy. Mummy Pig doesn't know who Leo is. "He's Suzy's pretend friend," explains Peppa.

Mummy gets an extra chair and a plate for Leo, then asks if he would like some fruit cake. "ROAR! Yes!" says Peppa, giggling. "Don't be silly, Peppa. That was you," says Suzy. "Leo doesn't like fruit cake." "I see," says Mummy Pig.

Play with Peppa

Peppa wants to play with you!
Here are some ideas for
perfect piggy games.

Noisy Time

Watch an episode of Peppa Pig and
pick one of these characters.
If some of your friends are
watching with you, they can
choose who they want to be too.
George
Suzy Sheep
Peppa Pig
Pedro Pony
When you spot your character on
the television, make their animal
noise. Watch out - you might end
up making a racket!

Piggy I-Spy

Look around the room.
Can you find five things
that are:
Pink like Peppa Pig?
Brown like Pedro Pony?
Black and white like Zoe Zebra?

Pigs Ahoy!

Peppa and George are on a boat
with Grandpa and Granny Pig.
Can you colour in the picture
using the colour key?

Colour key

1 Light blue 2 Pink 3 Purple

4 Dark blue 5 Yellow 6 Brown

3

5

1

2

4

Go to: www.peppapig.com/annualcolouring
for more Peppa colouring fun!

It's Snowing!

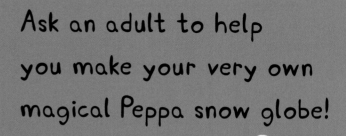

Ask an adult to help you make your very own magical Peppa snow globe!

You will need:
- A water-tight glass jar
- Snow scene from page 61
- Safe scissors
- Glitter

1. Carefully cut out the snow scene on page 61. If the scene doesn't fit around your jar you could draw you own.

2. Tape your scene around the outside of the back of your jar.

3. Fill your jar with water and some of your favourite coloured glitter.

4. Screw the lid of your jar on tightly and shake it around to make a lovely snow scene for Peppa and her family!

Cuckoo Clock

It's early morning and Mummy and Daddy Pig are asleep. "Snore! Snore!"
"Wakey! Wakey!" cries Peppa. "It's time to get up."
"It's much too early!" says Daddy. "Don't you know what time it is?"
"No, Daddy! Our clock doesn't work," replies Peppa.

"Let me see if I can fix the old cuckoo clock," says Daddy.
"Why is it called a cuckoo clock?" asks Peppa.
"There's a little wooden bird inside called a cuckoo," replies Mummy Pig.
"I've never seen the cuckoo," cries Peppa.
"We stopped winding it a long time ago," explains Daddy. "It got a bit annoying!"

"Can we wind it up again, please?" asks Peppa.
"All right then," replies Daddy, beginning to wind up the clock.
"There we go! You'll see the cuckoo very soon!"
"What does she look like, Daddy?" asks Peppa.

"Well, she moves her head like this . . ." says Daddy, pushing his head out.
"And she flaps her wings like this . . ." cries Daddy, waving his arms up and down. "Cuckoo!"
"Ha! Ha! Snort! Snort!" laugh Peppa and George. George runs around pretending to be a cuckoo.

"Look!" gasps Peppa, hearing a whirring noise.
"The clock's going to do something . . ." Cuckoo!
"Wow!" shouts Peppa, surprised.

Oh dear! George was so busy running
around pretending to be a cuckoo,
he missed the real one!
"Silly George," cries Peppa.
"You missed cuckoo."
"Never mind George! You can see
cuckoo next time," says Daddy.

George goes outside to play with
Peppa and Mr Dinosaur.
"Grrr! Dine-saw!" When he comes back
in he has missed the cuckoo again!
George bursts into tears.
"I'll call you when it's time
to see cuckoo," says Mummy Pig.

George goes out to play and then Mummy Pig cries,
"Peppa! George! Time to see cuckoo!"
George runs inside faster than he has ever run before.
He gets there just in time to see the cuckoo spring out of the clock.

"Grunt! Snort! Uckoo!" shouts George.
"Cuckoo! Snort!" cries Peppa.
Peppa and George love playing cuckoos!

is night time and Peppa and George are very
tired. They fall asleep very quickly. Cuckoo!
"Grunt!" snorts Peppa, waking up.
"Is it morning already?"
"No, no," says Daddy, taking the clock off the
all and putting it on the table. "Cuckoo is not
well, she needs sleep."

After Mummy and Daddy Pig go to bed,
Peppa has an idea. She wakes George up.
"Let's wind cuckoo up and make her
feel better!" she says, beginning to
wind up the clock.

Peppa and George run into Mummy and
Daddy's room. They are asleep.
"Mummy! Daddy!" whispers Peppa.
We've got something to show you. We've made
uckoo better!" Mummy and Daddy wake up to
the sound of the clock . . . Cuckoo!
"Ha, ha, ha! Snort! Snort!"
everyone laughs together.

What's the Time, Peppa?

Draw the right time on each clock as you find out what Peppa is doing.

Peppa and George clean their teeth at seven o'clock.

The post arrives at eight o'clock.

Peppa goes to school at nine o'clock.

Peppa and George play
outside at three o'clock.

Everyone has a
cup of tea at
half past four.

Peppa and George
go to bed at half
past seven.

Cut Out Clock

Make this Peppa Pig clock and learn how to tell the time!

You will need:

Safe scissors   Glue   Thin card   A paper fastener

What to do:

1. When you've finished reading this book, ask an adult to help you pull out the opposite page and stick it onto card.

2. Cut out the clock and hands along the dotted lines.

3. Press your paper fastener through the holes on the clock hands and then through the centre of the clock.

4. Now, move the hands around until they show the correct time and decorate your clock with stickers!

Granny and Grandpa's Attic

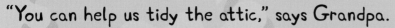

Today, Peppa and George
are playing at Granny and
Grandpa Pig's house.

"You can help us tidy the attic," says Grandpa.

"What's an attic?" asks Peppa.

"It's where we keep all our old things," replies Grandpa.

"Old like you, Grandpa?" smiles Peppa, cheekily.

"Ha, ha," laughs Grandpa. "Things that are even older than me, Peppa!"

The attic is at the very top of the house.

"Wow!" gasps Peppa. "It's very full!"

"Let's throw this out," says Granny, holding up a bottle.

"That's my ship in a bottle. I need it," replies Grandpa. "How about this box?"

"No!" cries Granny. "That has my hats inside it."

Oh dear. Granny and Grandpa can't decide what to throw out.

"Let's throw away this old case," suggests Peppa.
"Not that!" shout Granny and Grandpa together! "That's a record player."
Granny and Grandpa play their favourite music on the record player.
Crackle, crackle.
Peppa, George, Granny and Grandpa dance round and round the room!

"That was so much fun!" smiles Grandpa. "But we are supposed to be
finding things to throw out!"
"Hmmm, I think you should just keep . . . everything!" cries Peppa.
"Ha, ha, ha!" everyone laughs.

Counters and Spinner

For pages 20-21

Carefully cut out the counters and spinner along the dotted lines. Ask an adult to put a blunt pencil through the centre of the spinner.

Snow Scene

For pages 48-49

Cut out this cute Peppa snow scene along the dotted lines.